Usborne

First Colouring Book

Nativity

This book belongs to

_____

A long time ago, Joseph and Mary had to go to Bethlehem to put their names on a register. Mary was expecting a baby.

In Bethlehem everywhere was full, but an innkeeper said they could stay in his stable.

That night Mary's baby was born. She named
him Jesus and made a bed for him in the hay.

In the hills above Bethlehem some shepherds saw a bright light. It was a lovely angel.

Add these stickers to the pictures if you want.

Use these stickers on the last page.

Baby Jesus

Star

Mary

Joseph

Shepherds

Donkey

Three wise men

Sheep

"I have good news," said the angel.
"A baby has been born who is the
Son of God. You'll find him in a stable."

Then the sky was filled with beautiful angels singing joyfully.

Far away three wise men saw a bright star moving in the sky. They started to follow it.

The wise men followed the star
to Bethlehem and found Jesus.
They gave him presents.

That is the story of the first Christmas.
People call it the Nativity Story.

Use the stickers to make your own
Nativity scene.